The Kitten Who Wants to Say Goodbye to Diapers

A Story to Help Children Use The Potty

Leaves of Gold Press

Copyright © Leaves of Gold Press 2015

National Library of Australia Cataloguing-in-Publication entry

Creator: Leaves of Gold Press - author.

Title: The kitten who wants to say goodbye to diapers : a story to help children use the potty / Leaves of Gold Press ; Elizabeth Alger, illustrator.

ISBN: 978-1-925110-93-7 (paperback)

Target Audience:

Subjects: Kittens--Juvenile fiction.
Sleep--Juvenile fiction.
Stories in rhyme.

Dewey Number: A823.3

ABN 67 099 575 078
PO Box 9113, Brighton, 3186, Victoria, Australia
www.leavesofgoldpress.com

TO ADULTS:

What is different about this children's toilet training book?

It uses language patterns and proven, powerful psychological techniques that really get results. Motivation is the key to toilet training. This story is designed to be gently persuasive on both the conscious and unconscious levels.

When you think about toilet training your child, just relax. Feel calm and confident about your child's potty training. Just as children learn to talk and walk, so they learn to use the toilet. It might happen immediately or it might happen later, but they will learn.

For you, the parent or guardian, being relaxed is important. Have faith in Mother Nature. Trust that your child will eventually be toilet trained.

If you remain calm and confident your child will sense that confidence, and this can help their training. They may associate calmness with going to the toilet, and become relaxed about it themselves.

They may also sense that they cannot use their toilet training to exert control over you and begin a parent-child power struggle.

'Most children who are resistant to toilet training are enmeshed in a power struggle with their parents.'[1]

Creating positive attitudes to potty training is the key.

Never force a child to use the potty. Forcing children to do *anything* is likely to make them want to resist. It can also teach children to fear or dislike the potty. Instead, use positive motivation.

While children are learning to use the potty, never scold them for 'accidents'. They are doing their best. Scolding can make children think negatvely about potty-training.

After the child is daytime potty-trained, continue to use diapers at night during sleep-time, until the child decides that he or she no longer needs them.

How to read the story

This story is meant to be read aloud to children by an older person. It is intended as an aid to any effective potty-training method. The psychological techniques woven into this tale can make training quicker and easier. Simple rhyming verses add an extra element of fun.

---

1   Barton D. Schmitt, MD., "Toilet Training Problems: Underachievers, refusers, and stool holders." Contemporary Pediatrics 2004.

You can even read the story to babies. You'd be surprised how much they can understand – especially if they look at the pictures!

Because the story is intended for very young children whose attention spans may not be very long, it is relatively short and simple.

Read this story calmly, but be ready to laugh if you feel like it! It could be one of the most helpful and effective stories you've ever read.

Here's a tip: To make potty training easier for your child, make sure he or she is regularly eating nutritious fiber rich foods that will promote good digestion. Soft stools that can be passed comfortably will make it easier for your child to learn to use the potty.

Here and there throughout the book you will find instructions about making certain gestures or inserting the name of the child or children to whom you are reading the story. These instructions are contained in square brackets like this: [name].

In this book, words or phrases written in **bold** should be read out with special emphasis, while <u>underlined</u> words or phrases should be read out slowly and soothingly.

Interactivity

To help children learn, the story is interactive. You can read out questions for the child to answer, and you can ask the child to point to images on the pages.

You and the child can participate in a powerful and useful interactive activity just before you sit down together to read the story. Simply sing a simple action-rhyme song which names some body parts. This is a great way to have fun with your child and ensure a close rapport.

Singing body-part action songs has two benefits. Firstly, when children are stimulated into a happy, wakeful state with faster blood circulation, they are better able to learn. Secondly, when children can name some parts of their body it is easier for them to be successfully toilet trained.

Such action songs can include the well-known "Heads, Shoulders, Knees and Toes", the not-so-well-known but hilarious "Ankles, Elbows, Feet and Seat" (sung to the tune of "London Bridge") and other variations. The lyrics can be found in the addendum at the end of this book, along with some web-links to online videos.

Engaging in action songs is a way of reinforcing the child's awareness of body parts and their names, while strengthening your bond with the child and putting the child into a happy, alert state, ready to learn from the story.

"Matching movement to speech helps children move rhythmically and helps link thoughts and actions."[2]

Potty-training Readiness

"Potty-training success hinges on physical and emotional readiness, not a specific age. Many kids show interest in potty training by age 2, but others might not be ready until age 2 1/2 or even older..."[3]

---

2   Margaret Sasse, "Smart Start: How Exercise Can Transform Your Child's Life." 2009.

3   Mayo Clinic, "Potty Training: How to get the job done." 2014.

Brazelton[4] asserts that for true potty training, children must be able to:
- sit up by themselves
- walk, so that they can independently leave the potty chair
- have some understanding of verbal communication

Whether you decide to start training your child earlier or later, you can help him or her get ready. You can make toilet training easier and more pleasant for everyone by actively preparing your child. Reading this story to the child will help.

Universal Potty-Training Motivations

Motivations are powerful psychological tools. Many concepts are common to all potty-training methods. They are based on motivations that are natural in all healthy children.

These include:
- Imitation – seeing a person or a 'drink and wet' doll using a toilet or potty and wanting to copy. Imitation is a powerful psychological tool.
- Wanting to be independent and feel like a grown- up
- Peer pressure – seeing siblings or other toddlers successfully using the potty
- Wanting to be praiseworthy
- Wanting to feel dry
- Wanting to feel clean

---

4   Brazelton TB and Sparrow JD, "Toilet Training the Brazelton Way." Cambridge, MA: deCapo Press 2004.

Which Training Method is Best?

It is up to parents and guardian to decide which method is best for their child. Some of the most popular potty training methods are listed in the addendum at the back of this book.

For now just relax, read the story to your child, laugh, sing, and enjoy watching your little one achieve the milestones of growing up.

Happy reading!

The Kitten Who Wants to Say Goodbye to Diapers

While you listen to me reading this story you will learn how to **use the potty** easily. Perhaps you will learn without even realising you are doing it. You might learn how to **use the potty** today, or it might take longer. I wonder whether you will learn how to **use the potty** after you hear the story the first time, or after you hear it a few times.

Do you sometimes think about how uncomfortable diapers make you feel when they are wet or dirty? When you can use the potty you won't have to wear them any more! Everyone will know how clever and grown-up you are! Can you imagine <u>how much better you will feel</u> when you can **use the potty** easily?

Mopsi was a little kitten who wanted to learn how to use the potty. She was too small to use the toilet like her big sister Misti, but she wanted to learn to use the potty easily, instead of wearing diapers. She wanted to say goodbye to diapers.

Mopsi was just like you, [name]. She like to play games ,and play with toys, and have fun. She liked to listen to stories, just as you are doing right now! She also liked to eat Mommy's yummy food. You like yummy food too, don't you [name]?

Mopsi's favorite food was apple pie. Can you imagine the delicious smell of pie straight from the oven? Mmmm! When there was apple pie for dinner Mommy would say, "Hooray, hooray! It's apple pie day!" As she said it she would throw up her arms, like this [raise your arms high into the air].

And Mopsi would throw up her arms too, and giggle.

Or if everyone was going to the park, Daddy might say, "Hooray, hooray! It's going to the park day!" And he would smile and throw his arms up into the air [raise your arms].

So whenever Misti and Mopsi felt very happy and excited they would shout "Hooray" and fling their arms in the air! Can you do that too, [name]?

One day Misti and Mopsi were playing a game together. Misti said, "Show me how clever you are, Mopsi. Where is your arm?"

Mopsi pointed to her arm.

"That's it!" cried Misti, who always spoke in a loud voice when she was happy. "Well done!"

Can you point to Mopsi's arm in the picture, [name]? Can you point to your arm? That's right!

"Where is your knee, Mopsi?" said Misti. Mopsi pointed to her knee.

"Yes!" shouted Misti. "Well done!"

Can you point to Mopsi's knee in the picture, [name]? Can you point to your knee? That's right!

"Wait a minute," said Misti, bouncing up and down. She squeezed her legs together. "I feel like I need to go pee. I have to **use the toilet**."

She ran to the bathroom, but Mopsi followed her.

"Looks as if I forgot to shut the door," said Misti, who was already sitting on the toilet. "What do you want, Mopsi?"

"Want to play 'where is'," said Mopsi.

"Well, okay. Where is your bottom?" asked Misti

Mopsi pointed to her behind. She giggled.

"Clever you!" said Misti. "Well done! Now put your bottom on the potty chair and wait a minute!"

Mopsi **sat down on the potty chair**. She liked copying the things Misti did.

Misti finished using the toilet. She climbed down, pulled up her underpants and washed her hands at the basin. "Let's play a different game now," she said. "Go and get your Baby Maybee."

Mopsi went into her bedroom. When she came back she was carrying a baby doll. She handed it to Misti.

"Eeeuw!" said Misti. "Baby Maybee's diaper is wet! Have you been giving her drinks?

Mopsi nodded her head. [Nod your head.]

"Your dolly doesn't like having a wet bottom," said Misti.

She helped Mopsi change Baby Maybee's wet diaper for a clean, dry one.

"Now she's dry," said Misti. "She <u>feels better now</u>, doesn't she Mopsi?"

Mopsi nodded her head again.

"We have to teach Baby Maybee how to stay dry," said Misti. "She must learn to **use the potty**. Can you give her another drink?"

Mopsi gave Baby Maybee another bottle of water.

Misti said, "I think Baby Maybee feels like she has to pee now," said Misti. "Take off her diaper and sit her on the potty chair!"

Mopsi took off Baby Maybee's diaper. When she put the doll on the potty chair, she picked her up straight away, and looked into the potty. It was empty.

"No, you have to wait!" said Misti. "She needs some time to use the potty. Put her back!"

Misti liked being Mopsi's teacher. It made her feel important.

Mopsi put Baby Maybee back on the potty chair, and everyone waited for a minute.

"Now look again," said Misti. "Is anything in the potty?"

Mopsi picked up Baby Maybee and had a look in the potty. She nodded. "Ess!" she said. That is how Mopsi says 'yes'.

Misti hugged the doll. "Clever Baby Maybee! You used the potty easily! I think she is old enough to wear undies now, don't you, Mopsi?"

Mipsi said 'Ess," and fetched some spare underpants for her doll.

Carefully, so as not to spill any water, Misti picked up the potty and emptied it into the toilet.

Misti helped Mopsi put on Baby Maybee's clean, dry underpants, and then they both washed their hands.

"Are her undies still dry?" Misti asked Mopsi.

Mopsi placed her paw on the doll's underpants, then nodded again. "Ess!"

"Yes! Clever Baby Maybee!" said Misti. "Big kids don't wet their pants. Baby Maybee is a big kid now! She can use the potty easily!"

"Hooray!" shouted Mopsi, lifting her arms toward the ceiling.

"Hooray, hooray, it's potty day!" cried Misti, throwing up her arms, too. "It's potty day for Baby Maybee!"

Mopsi did a happy dance.

"Would you like to give your dolly another drink?" asked Misti.

But Mopsi shook her head, meaning 'no'. She started jiggling around and grabbing at her diaper. She squeezed her legs together and made a funny face.

Misti said, "Hey Mopsi it looks like you need to pee or poop. You should use the potty!"

You know that feeling you get when you need to use the potty, don't you, [name]?

But it was too late, because Mopsi was already hiding behind the sofa. After a while Misti heard her say, "Mopsi go pee."

When Mopsi came out from behind the sofa her face was all screwed up and she looked disgusted. She started trying to pull off her diapers. "Wet," she said. "I don't want it."

[Name], can you point to the picture of which diaper Mopsi likes best- a wet one or a dry one?

You are right! Being dry feels better, doesn't it?[5]

Just then, Mommy came into the room.

"Mommy, Mopsi's diaper is wet," said Misti. "She needs changing."

"Thanks Misti," said Mommy. She picked up Mopsi and put her on the changing table. After she removed the wet diaper, she cleaned Mopsi.

---

5   If children choose the wrong picture say, "Really? Are you sure?" If they continue to choose the wrong one say, "I think you're just playing! It's this one!" and point it out.

Mopsi looked happy to be clean and dry. <u>She was feeling more comfortable now.</u>

"Hey Mopsi, when I do poops and pees I use the toilet," said Misti. "That's because I am more grown-up than you. I can wear pants, not diapers."

Mopsi stopped looking happy. She frowned.

Mommy said, "Mopsi, would you like to try wearing training pants today?"

"Ess," said Mopsi, smiling again.

So Mommy put training pants on her instead of diapers. She lifted Mopsi off the changing table and went into the bathroom to wash her hands.

Later that day Misti went to the toilet again. As she was sitting there, she remembered that she had forgotten to close the door again. Just then, Mopsi toddled in.

"What are you doing in here Mopsi?" Misti asked. "It's supposed to be private when people use the toilet."

Mopsi pulled down her new training pants and sat on the potty chair. She was looking very proud of herself.

"Ooh, Clever! You can **use the potty**, just like a grown-up kitten," said Misti admiringly. Mopsi looked happier than ever, and very proud to be acting like her big sister.

There was nothing in the potty when Mopsi stood up, but Mommy and Misti were proud of her anyway.

The next day Misti and Mopsi were playing with play-dough in the kitchen, pretending to make apple pies, while Mommy was washing some dishes at the sink.

All of a sudden Mopsi made that funny face again. She started to bounce around a bit, and she crossed her legs.

"Hey, it looks as if you need to pee," said Misti.

[Name], what should Mopsi do when she feels like she needs to pee?

Should she go to the park and and play on the swings?
No!
Should she have something to eat?
No!
Should she look at a picture book?
No!
Should she pull down her undies and sit on the potty?
Yes!

"Mommy!" said Misti, "Mopsi needs to use the potty!"

Mommy looked around. She took Mopsi by the hand and led her to the bathroom. Mopsi pulled down her training pants and sat on the potty chair.

After a while Mopsi stood up. She and Mommy looked into the potty. Something that looked like water was in there. But it wasn't water!

"Well done, Mopsi!" said Mommy. "You have learned how to **use the potty**!"

Mopsi had the biggest smile ever on her face. She was feeling very proud of herself.

Mommy helped her pull up her training pants and wash her hands.

Then Misti put her head around the bathroom door.

"Did you use the potty?" she asked her little sister.

"Ess," said Mopsi.

"Hey, you're a big kitten!" said Misti. She threw up her arms. "Hooray, hooray! It's potty day!"

Mommy and Mopsi laughed and joined in. They threw their arms into the air too, and shouted, "Hooray, hooray! It's potty day!"

And from that day, Mopsi knew how to use the potty.

Sometimes when she was still practising she got wet underpants when she didn't make it to the potty on time, but that didn't matter. Nobody gets everything perfect as soon as they learn something new. After a few weeks she got it right every time. Mommy and Daddy and Misti were <u>more and more proud of her</u>.

But proudest of all was Mopsi herself!

The Potty Poem

Diaper rash makes your butt itchy and spotty,
But you don't get that when you use the potty!
When you can sit on the potty to pee,
Diaper rash goes away quickly – you'll see!

Diapers get dirty and sometimes smell bad
Using the potty makes Mopsi feel glad
She's like those big kids – she does what they do
She's good at using the potty – are you?

Mopsi says,
"I use the potty 'cause I am so clever.
"I plan on having dry undies forever.
"As soon as I feel like I'm going to pee,
"I sit on the potty. It's easy for me!

"Ev'rything's nicer when you're clean and dry,
"So I use the potty now – diapers goodbye!"

Addendum

At what age should your child start toilet training?

Even though your child's age at the outset of training is not as important as their physical and emotional readiness, it is still relevant.

If a child is too old, the process may be harder to learn. Older children may be rebellious, or may be accustomed to wearing a wet or dirty diaper. Having learned to ignore their body's signals, they must now become aware of them. Children who are learning to walk may be too excited to sit still on a potty chair.[6] One study found that children who started training after the age of 24 months risked slower progress and more setbacks.[7]

Contrary to popular belief, modern scientific studies suggest that early training does not cause problems. On the other hand, if children start toilet training too young, they may have little or no muscular control over the elimination process.

The main disadvantage for children who begin earlier is that they usually take longer to complete training.

One study showed that it took an average of 13-14 months to train children who started the training between 18-24 months of age.

---

6   Brazelton TB and Sparrow JD. "Toilet Training the Brazelton Way." Cambridge, MA: deCapo Press 2004.

7   Joinson C, Heron J, Von Gontard A, Butler U, Emond A, Golding J. "A prospective study of age at initiation of toilet training and subsequent daytime bladder control in school-age children." J Dev Behav Pediatr. 30(5):385-93. 2009.

By contrast it took 10 months or less to train children who began after the age of 27 months. This implies that there is little to be gained from starting to toilet train children between the ages of 18 and 27 months.[8]

If you have chosen to leave toilet training until your child is 18 months or older, you can use the intervening time for preparation.

Children aged 12-18 months can learn skills and concepts that will help them enormously when it comes time for training. Reading stories to them — such as the story in this book — can help.

Choose your training method

"There's no single, guaranteed method for success in potty training. You've got to choose your strategy based on the kind of kid your child is, and the kind of parent you are, too."[9]

There are numerous popular methods of toilet training, each with its own pros and cons. The opinions of experts on this topic are divided. Some authorities advocate early training, others recommend late. Some say training should be child-led, others say that parent-led training is preferable. Some say that candy and other treats should be used as an incentive, while others urge avoiding 'rewards' at all costs.

---

8   Blum NJ, Taubman B, and Nemeth N., "Relationship between age at initiation of toilet training and duration of training: A prospective study." Pediatrics, 111: 810-814. 2003.

9   Stephanie Wood, "6 Potty Training Methods." www.parenting. com/gallery/potty-training-methods. Retrieved 7th Oct 2015.

Signs of readiness for potty-training

Dr Sears[10] advises that your toddler is ready for toilet training when he or she:

- Imitates your toileting
- Verbally communicates other sensations, such as hunger
- Understands simple requests, such as "go get ball"
- Begins to pull diapers off when wet or soiled, or comes to tell you he's dirty
- Follows you to the bathroom
- Is able to pull clothes off
- Climbs onto the potty-chair or toilet
- Has dry spells: stays dry at least three hours

The general sequence of potty training:

- Seeing others using the toilet and imitating them.
- Learning to be aware of the urge to eliminate.
- Sitting on the potty when the urge occurs.
- If the expected event does not occur immediately, waiting patiently until it does.
- If there's success, getting praise for it.
- If no success, being reassured that it's okay and being praised for trying and reassured that they can try again next time.
- Wiping.
- Pulling up pants.
- Washing hands.
- Adult disposes of waste.

---

10   Dr Sears "6 Steps for Toddler Toilet Training." http://www.askdr-sears.com 2015.

If there's an accident at any time during the training period, the adult should shows no emotion — neither praise nor criticism. The child should be reassured that what has happened is okay. He or she should be praised for trying, and reassured that they can try again next time. ("Sometimes it's hard to get to the potty in time. That's okay. We'll help you clean up.")

Some popular potty training techniques

Infant potty training: 0-12 months of age

1. *"Elimination communication".*
This method is widely practised with very young babies in the non-Western world. Strictly speaking this is not potty training because the babies are too young to walk to the potty. No diapers are worn.

The method relies on parents being in such close and constant communication with their child that they can learn to recognise the signals the child makes when he or she is about to eliminate. The parent then holds the baby over a suitable receptacle while the process takes place.

In many parts of the world, such as China, India and South-east Asia, this method is widely practised. Parents carry their babies with them practically all the time. While elimination communication bypasses dealing with diapers and diaper rash, it requires constant commitment from parents.

2. *The Smeets method for infant potty training.*

This method is sometimes called the 'potty chair method' or 'self-initiated potty training'. Paul Smeets and his colleagues tested their procedure on four children aged 3-6 months. [11]

After 18 months of age

Gradual, parent-led toilet training.

There are a few variations of this method. One example is Dr. Barton D. Schmitt's version. Schmitt says "Studies have shown that more than 90% of children show signs of readiness between 18 and 30 months of age".[12]

Around 20 months or older

1. *Toilet training in less than a day and other 'accelerated' methods.*

These techniques are intended for children aged 20 months or more who have had no previous toilet training. They have a good success rate, but only if parents and guardians make sure they are fully prepared and that they thoroughly understand the instructions before they begin. Bear in mind that not all children respond to this method.

11　　Smeets PM, Lancioni GE, Ball, TS, and Oliva DS. "Shaping self-initiated toileting in infants." Journal of applied behavior analysis, 18: 303-308. 1985.
12　　Provided by McKenzie Pediatrics, "Dr. Barton Schmitt's Toilet Training Guidelines For Parents." 2007.

2. *John Rosemond's 'Naked and $75' method.*

This method gets its name because the child is allowed to be as naked as possible during the training period, but parents will probably need $75 to clean the carpets when the inevitable accidents occur. Rosemond suggests toilet training children between the ages of 18 and 24 months, but no older. Rosemond's principles are very different from those of Brazelton.[13]

Pediatrician Dr. Barton Schmitt recommends Rosemond's approach for children over 30 months who have already used the potty with parental assistance.[14]

3. *Potty training the Brazelton way*

This child-oriented potty training method is usually associated with late training. Brazelton and recommends delaying potty training until the child voluntarily shows specific signs of being ready. After the parent or guardian notices these signs, they embark on a sequence of steps whose timing is set by the child.

---

13   Erica Goode, "Two Experts Do Battle Over Potty Training."New York Times. Published: January 12, 1999.
14   Schmitt BA. "Toilet training: Getting it right the first time." Contemporary Pediatrics, 21: 105-119, and Schmitt BA. 2004. Toilet training problems: Underachievers, refusers, and stool holders. Contemporary Pediatrics, 21: 71-82. 2004.

Action Songs

Heads, Shoulders Knees and Toes

This action song has four versions. Choose which one suits you best!

Version 1 is sung to the tune of "There is a Tavern in the Town". As you name each body part, you touch it with both hands. Try singing the song slowly the first time and quicker the second time.

Heads, shoulders knees and toes, knees and toes,
Heads, shoulders knees and toes, knees and toes,
And eyes and ears and mouth and nose,
Heads, shoulders knees and toes, knees and toes.

Version 2 is also sung to the tune of "There is a Tavern in the Town".

Cheeks, chin and neck and bum, neck and bum,
Cheeks, chin and neck and bum, neck and bum,
And eyebrows, back, belly and thumbs,
Cheeks, chin and neck and bum, neck and bum,

Version 3 is sung to its own tune, which you can hear online. It finishes with a round of applause!
www.youtube.com/watch?v=QYjhoM41zmA

Heads and shoulders, knees and toes,
Knees and toes, knees and toes,
Heads and shoulders, knees and toes,
We all clap hands together!

Version 4 is sung to the tune of "London Bridge"

Head and shoulders, knees and toes,
Knees and toes,
Knees and toes,
Head and shoulders, knees and toes,
It's my body

Eyes and ears and mouth and nose,
Mouth and nose,
Mouth and nose,
Eyes and ears and mouth and nose,
It's my body

Ankles, elbows, feet and seat,
Feet and seat,
Feet and seat,
Ankles, elbows, feet and seat,
It's my body

About the Series

This book is part of a series called "The Kitten Who ...".

The much-loved bedtime story 'The Kitten Who Wants To Fall Asleep" and the popular children's anger-management story "The Kitten Who Wants To Be The Boss Of Her Temper" are highly effective and helpful tools for parents.

Other books in the series 'The Kitten Who ...'

The Kitten Who Wants to Fall Asleep:
A Story To Help Children Go To Sleep

Children sometimes find it hard to get to sleep.

What if you could read them a bedtime story incorporating powerful psychological methods to help them fall asleep quickly, easily and without drugs?

Psychological sleep induction techniques include:
- putting aside your thoughts until the following day
- breathing deeply
- slowing down
- visualizing a safe and peaceful place
- imagining a descent with the sensation of sinking
- progressive muscle relaxation
- using sleep-triggering words
- employing the 'infectiousness' of yawning.

Such methods are well-known and can be found in libraries or by searching for 'psychological sleep techniques' on the Internet.

This book also uses the hypnotic power of rhyme and rhythm. Songs and lullabies have traditionally been used to lull children to sleep. 'Hypnotic' poetry works in much the same way.

The poems in this book are in the relaxing, calming rhythm called 3/4 time, better known as 'waltz time'. All parents know that gentle, rocking rhythms can soothe a child.

The rhyming is as important as the rhythm. Children love poems that rhyme. For them, rhyming words make poetry fun and memorable.

Just as children respond to soothing rhythms and imagery, so they can fall asleep while listening to the tale of Misti the Kitty.

The Kitten
Who Wants
To Fall Asleep

A Story To Help Children Go To Sleep

Cecilia Egan
Illustrated by Elizabeth Alger

Other books in the series 'The Kitten Who ...'

The Kitten Who Wants to be the Boss of her Temper:
A Story to Help Children Deal With Tantrums

What if you could read your children a story incorporating effective psychological methods to help them learn to manage anger?

Many parents worry about young children behaving aggressively when they feel upset. Much of this is normal for youngsters. Nevertheless, these issues do need to be addressed.

Psychological anger management techniques include:

'Breathing out' the anger with slow, deep breaths.

Counting to ten slowly, to give angry feelings some time to subside.

Moving away from the problem situation until you feel calmer.

Squeezing or pummelling a soft, inanimate object such as a cushion, which cannot be hurt and which cannot hurt you.

Engaging in vigorous physical activities such as running, cycling, dancing or even housework, as an outlet for pent-up feelings.

Lying down and listening to relaxing music, or sleeping.

When you feel calmer, talking about your feelings with someone you trust.

This story also harnesses the mnemonic power of visual association and simple rhyming verse to make learning fun and the techniques easier to remember.

Just as children respond to Cecilia Egan's sleep-inducing story 'The Kitten Who Wants to Fall Asleep," so they can learn to be the boss of their temper while listening to this tale.

The Kitten Who Wants To Be The Boss of Her Temper

A Story to Help Children Deal With Tantrums

Cecilia Egan
Illustrated by Elizabeth Alger